Ponderful Poems

for

Challenging Children

by

Thomas N. Thornton

First published in 1997 by

TCOJ Publishers
1, South View
Uppingham
Rutland, LE15 9TU
Fax: 01572-822994
e-mail: T.N.T@btinternet.com

Printed and bound in England by
Woolnough Bookbinding Ltd
Irthlingborough, Northants NN9 5SE

ISBN 0 9531665 0 3

To all God's Children,

including my own dear
Charles, Oliver and James,
and any others of mine,
born or unborn, seen or unseen,
real, unreal or imaginary,
alleged or adopted

There is no Foreword or Introduction to this book. If I had not ignored the boring bits at the beginning of books, I would have been a lot older before I read anything interesting. Here are just a few words of guidance.

These poems start with the youngest first and progress. You may have to be a middle-aged child before you fully understand 'The Other Open Prison'.

Get some help with difficult words, or preferably get someone to read to you, which is particularly nice before you go to sleep.

Skip any poems that do not appeal to you at present. They may mean something more later, so don't dismiss them completely.

The verses are short, so that you can pause easily to ponder. The type and spacing change, so as to give variety to the eye and the imagination.

You should almost think that you have written some of these rhymes. They are here to demonstrate that verses can be written on any subject, not just Daffodils, Unrequited Love and Death. Try it.

Forward, brothers and sisters! Read on................

Contents

Bedtime beginners

Goodnight to Arms
>For when the sheep run out

Wish I were a bird
>For when the wind is howling round the house

Mars Lander
>For when you are feeling other-worldly

Music Calleth
>For when you just need to dream

Growing older slowly

Eternal Youth
> For those uncertain that schooldays are best

Childhood lost
> For those who have forgotten their schooldays already

Live it up
> For action, after consulting the elderly

Examining material things

Woe to the Motor Car
> The grown-up's toy which is enslaving us

Reflections in the Sand
> Thoughts on one of Nature's curiosities

Something and Nothing
> What lurks within the Computer

Chronological perspective

Greenwich Mean Time
> Changing times, where East meets West

Less frivolous verses interspersed with funny tales

Food for Thought
> For future digestive action

Hilda Hypochondria
> Everyone has, or will, meet someone like this

The Spirit of Adventure
> Seeking directions

Odd, No God
> For those who may have already dismissed their Maker

What stirs within?
> An embarrassing tale that many travellers will understand

Love is ...... or isn't it?
> A checklist for the wannabe romantic

Genius
> For those not already certain that they qualify

The Other Open Prison
> A destination that some may have visited,
> which others should seek to avoid

The Toast

Holograms or Holocaust
> A hopeful plea for the future

Goodnight to Arms

Please, God, I need your assistance
      What can I do with my arms?
They've been so useful since breakfast
      I'm fully versed with their charms

But when it comes round to bedtime
      That's when I'm filled with dismay
Where can I put them when sleeping?
      They seem to get in the way

Mum says I'm best on my right side
      But where can I put my right arm?
Why not just there, straight behind me
      Where it can't do too much harm?

I'm drifting off nicely to dreamland
      Oh now - what's this mess that I'm in?
The pillow has slipped out from under
      And all of my weight's on my chin

I'll try the left arm on the pillow
      With the left knee to balance the weight
That must be what mother intended
      So how could I get in that state?

I'm back to my slumbers in earnest
　　　　But I've run out of numbers and sheep
And now I'm awake, what's the trouble?
　　　　Ah yes, only my left arm's asleep

I'll try turning over completely
　　　　And mirror the same in reverse
I may not find this any better
　　　　But then it can't be any worse

At first this solution seems perfect
　　　　But maybe the right side was best
For instead of the sheep I was counting
　　　　It is now the heartbeats in my chest

I'll try lying flat on my stomach
　　　　With an arm neatly stretched either side
But my neck's twisted this way or that way
　　　　And my toes don't know quite where to hide

I'll lie on my back for a moment
　　　　With arms crossed, the better to think
But the thoughts are now coming more slowly
　　　　As down into slumber I sink

Oh God, that's an angel that's calling
　　　　Or is it the voice of my Dad?
Saying, 'Come on now, sleep on your right side
　　　　Your snores have woke Mother, young lad'

So back to Square One with reluctance
        Right arm underneath, round my waist
With the other arm clutching my Teddy
        To my chest he is firmly embraced

The night seems to flash past in moments
        I wake in the cold of the dawn
And I hear shrieks of laughter behind me
        As I try hard to stifle a yawn

'Oh, what are you laughing at, Mummy?'
        She said, 'What are you doing there
With your head buried under the pillow
        And your little bare bum in the air?'

I told her the problem I'd suffered
        How my arms seemed to get in the way
And she promised to find a solution
        By tonight, if it took her all day

I can only think what she's intending
        To fulfil this most fiendish of oaths
Is to take my arms out of their sockets
        And hang them up next to my clothes

Wish I were a Bird

When it's stormy and it's squalling

    And conditions are appalling

        It is then that I most wish I were a bird

I would sit upon a steeple

    Far away from all those people

        Who keep telling me, 'Be seen and not be heard'

When the gusts are quite disgusting

    I would start my filibustering

        I would spread my wings and rise up to the sky

I would twirl into a swirl

    Catching sight of some poor girl

        And then dive and try to splat her in the eye

To continue with the story

    I'd rise up again in glory

        Playing games with every cloud that came along

And then as the storm abated

    My ambitions satiated

        I'd come back to Earth and break into a song

Mars Lander

If you were to land in a spaceship
        You'd find it a funny old world
You'd find people fighting each other
        With all of their banners unfurled

If you were to land in a jungle
        It's doubtful how long you would last
Because you don't know all the secrets
        That natives have learnt in the past

If you were to land in a desert
        You'd get far too hot in the day
And during the night you'd be frozen
        The temperature changes that way

If you should descend in the Ocean
        You'd then be surrounded by sea
Unless you're a passable swimmer
        It's not such a good place to be

If you should descend in a palace
        You'll soon be surrounded by guards
Make sure that you check their credentials
        Young princes like playing charades

If you were to land in a prison
        Surrounded by inmates you'd be
You'd have to look after your spaceship
        For all of them want to be free

If a factory is where you have landed
        Try to choose one that makes chocolate bars
You've a fair chance to earn a free sample
        Just tell them you've come down from Mars

Should you chance to arrive in a city
        If room for your spaceship you find
It's here that you'll find concentrations
        Of what people call Human Kind

Now 'kind' is the strangest description
        For people who argue all day
Over, politics, sex and religion
        And even the games that they play

You may wonder why so many people
        Pack themselves into so little space
When there's so much spare land for the taking
        Well it seems such a blatant disgrace

You may ask, 'What on earth makes them cluster
       In squalid conditions like these
When there's glorious country abounding
       All covered with flowers and trees?'

'We did it at first for protection
       And then to develop our skills
To make our amazing contraptions
       And deal with our aches, pains and ills'

'You must have defeated your object
       To improve upon life, one assumes
For you now live on top of each other
       And your kids are all choking on fumes'

'Have you just come here to cause trouble?
       Come on, brothers, and let us unite
He has said that he's stating the obvious
       But he's obviously out for a fight'

'It's a shame you can't answer my questions
       I dropped in for a nice cup of tea
But I see you've polluted your rivers
       And your fish are all dying at sea

It seems you rely upon breathing
       And that requires lots of fresh air
It appears that you waste your breath talking
       When you should, for your atmosphere, care

To return to ecology balance
        You must clean up your factories and cars
You must plant trees to get rid of gasses
        We had problems like this once on Mars

Very soon you will find procreation
        Is becoming a thing of the past
If you carry on laughing at nature
        You'll find nature's the one that laughs last

To ruin your beautiful planet
        Would be such a dreadful disgrace
But, as we don't rely upon breathing
        It would make a fine holiday place

Now please put your gun down, young fellow
        Because here I have got a device
Which not only returns all your bullets
        But can vaporise you in a trice

I'd like to return to my spaceship
        So please, gentle folk, step aside
If you'd just been a little politer
        I'd have taken you up for a ride

I'm just on my way round to Venus
        To get a few things that we need
I will pop back to see how you're faring
        In the meantime, just wish me God Speed'

Music calleth

What's in a dance?
>What's in a song?
Did I hear music?
>Could I be wrong?

Yes, I heard music
>Where was the dance?
Was someone singing?
>Was it a trance?

Deep in the background
>Softly to start
Somewhere a melody
>Stirs in the heart

Open the window
>Yes, it is there
Follow the singing
>Don't stand and stare

Into the forest
>Follow the sound
Light through the branches
>Dew on the ground

Flames from the torches
        Sparks from the fire
Louder the music
        Higher and higher

Would I be welcome?
        No, I must hide
Here's a big tree trunk
        Peep round the side

There in the clearing
        As I look down
Eyes full of laughter
        Nowhere a frown

One side the players
        Flautists and drums
Then the guitarist
        Sings as he strums

This side the dancers
        Light on their feet
Twisting and weaving
        Smile as they meet

Cracking a twig
        Tapping my feet
Curse, I'm discovered
        I must retreat

Now I'm surrounded
        But they reach out
'Come join the party'
        Gladly they shout

Once in the clearing
        Everyone stands
Arms round my shoulders
        Clasping my hands

Guiding me gently
        One on each side
Feeling the rhythm
        Into my stride

Soon I am singing
        First just a snatch
Then as the words come
        Phrases I catch

Carried away now
      Dancing till dawn
Happy but sleepy
      Starting to yawn

Home before sunrise
      Farewells to say
'Come again next week'
      'Yes, if I may'

Back through the window
      Safe into bed
Still with the music
      Inside my head

What was I missing?
      Why was I slow?
Music and laughter
      Rearing to go

Still in my memory
      The song and the dance
Praying for next week
      Six days in advance

Eternal Youth

You often hear elderly people
     Saying, 'Wish I was young once again'
They're usually kindly old grandmas
     But I've heard the same thing said by men

Now, I'd like to be a bit older
     Because everything I want to do
Seems to need someone taller and stronger
     And there's often an age limit too

There must be a crafty solution
     And I've got some ideas that might work
But, if I let you into my secrets
     You'll probably laugh or just smirk

Now, my first wheeze requires a target
     And not just a boring old fart
He must be an interesting fellow
     Yet still want to be young at heart

I'll swop him a day of my childhood
     For a day in the life that he leads
Thus giving us each an experience
     That will cater for both of our needs

I could swop with a rich man for starters
     Go to Henley or Ascot or Lords
I'll be cruising around in his Roller
     Whilst he's fighting it out with the hordes

I might try a swop with a statesman
        But where would I find one of those
I'd just get a bent politician
        All corrupt to the end of his toes

I might try an ageing professor
        With wisdom enough and to spare
I'd fill up my brain with his knowledge
        To wake up next morning - not there

But turning to something exciting
        I'd swop with a racing car ace
Or even a brave fighter pilot
        Or an astronaut right out in space

But what if the person I swopped with
        So enjoyed his one day at my school
He refused to swop back after midnight
        To be sure, then I would look a fool

Now another idea that I thought of
        Was to say that I'm seventeen at least
And when asked, 'Did your mother not feed you?'
        I'd say, 'Yes, but she left out the yeast'

Or to enter a pact with the devil
        Is another incredible wheeze
Lend him four years at best rates of interest
        To be cashed in whenever I please

I can countenance dozens of wheezes
        But I must to the concept return
Why the old folk refer to their happiest days
        When I'm bored and I've got time to burn

Childhood Lost

Did you miss out on happiness?

Did happiness pass you by?

Did you not hear a crocus grow

Or laugh at a baby's cry?

Whatever happened to the sun

Which shone when you were a boy?

Whatever happened to the fun?

That heart that was beaming with joy?

Wherever went that glorious Moon

    Reflected on rivers and snow?

Wherever went all those magnificent trees

    And where did the animals go?

Whatever happened to all that space

    You rejoiced in when you were a lad?

And what did they do with that crystal air

    That filled up the lungs you once had?

Live it up

I've done some research into old folk
      Who want to be young once again
And some of it seems pretty senseless
      But some is remarkably sane

There is one group who want repetition
      For they certainly had lots of fun
And they still find a way to enjoy life
      Almost anywhere under the sun

But memory forms a delusion
      Whereby bad things fade faster than good
And so days as a child that seemed cloudless
      They were not, they would be if they could

Now, some folk with more honest memories
      Will tell of the bad times as well
And some who were truly unhappy
      Paint a pretty fair picture of hell

Then, a lot who aspire to be younger
      Want to change what they did first time round
But when faced with equivalent factors
      They'd repeat their mistakes, I'd be bound

And the places they walked in their childhood
        Are now covered in concrete and glass
So, could any second impressions
        Their first-time best moments surpass?

Hence, what I have learnt from these studies
        Well, that history began yesterday
And today will be gone by tomorrow
        When tomorrow's the following day

I have learnt from my elders and betters
        That each day seems much shorter with time
And to think life will go on for ever
        Is a mirage that's far too sublime

And it's clear that this urge to be younger
        All reflects on the time they misspent
'Cos they thought they would do things tomorrow
        But they can't, 'cos they're aged and bent

So, much chastened by this little lesson
        I've forgotten my urge to get old
And I've so many things to get on with
        I've not time for them all to be told

If you're bored and you want to be older
        Just remember you're only young once
Therefore, use every possible moment
        Or you'll look back and say, 'What a dunce!'

Wo*e* to the Motor Car

Oh Motor Car, Oh Motor Car
        Oh what a heart's delight you are
For since I was a little boy
        I've craved for such a grown-up's toy

That throbbing sound of thoroughbred
        Your racing tone went to my head
Reminded as I was of Toad
        His carefree spirit on the road

But now I'm old enough at last
        Those yearning dreams are in the past
No thoroughbred could I afford
        So find that I'm a trifle bored

My rusty rib goes well enough
        It's little engine is quite tough
It's safe and sound to get you there
        But hardly travels like a hare

And why does it depreciate?
        Those garage bills I've learnt to hate
Insurance, tax and parking fees
        With petrol brings me to my knees

And things have changed since I was young
        With modern drivers highly-strung
And accidents that were their fault
        Bring sleeves rolled up for an assault

Now where do all these people go
        Their worries, through their driving, show
For surely they don't all commute
        With briefcase and a City suit

They've hardly time to look around
        Lest someone on their horn should sound
With concentration on the road
        Their pace with roadworks often slowed

To visit friends I sometimes yearn
        But they're out driving in their turn
I long to sunbathe on a beach
        Which coastbound jams put out of reach

If others were to take the bus
        Then I could travel with less fuss
They'd use those InterCity trains
        If only they had any brains

Now bus routes that were made to pay
        Run once a year or twice a day
A branch line to a distant town
        Through motor cars is now closed down

These lumps of metal everywhere
        Make conservationists despair
Ecologists in vain protest
        In motor cars we still invest

It's many years since Man contrived
        To reach the Moon - and safe arrived
There was not much in his control
        Computers helped to reach this goal

But still today we are in charge
          Of vehicles both small and large
Permitted by the law, we go
          At seventy miles an hour or so

Towards each other down the lanes
          O'er pot-holes, ice and blocked-up drains
We speed without a thought to flinch
          And miss each other by an inch

A transport we must now invent
          With far less murderous intent
Which programmed to our destination
          Gets there with less protestation

Oh Motor Car, I am too late
          You're clearly past your sell-by date
No more a transport of delight
          You're suffering from traffic blight

That sense of venture Toad once felt
          The summer fragrance that he smelt
Are swallowed now by traffic queues
          And fumes enough to give the blues

Oh Motor Car, your time is up
          Your final petrol cup to sup
And to museums be confined
          Your joyous years left in the Mind

Reflections in the Sand

Seated on your desert island
    Waiting for a ship to pass
Whilst the sand runs through your fingers
    Marvel that it could be glass

Sand is glass's main ingredient
    Add some soda and some lime
Ponder how man came to find this
    Way back in the sands of time

Glass is unique as a product
    Needing much heat when it forms
When it's cooled, it makes good windows
    Keeping out the worst of storms

By manipulating glass whilst molten
    Still within a plastic state
It can form extreme contortions
    Or be stretched into a plate

As the glass is gently cooling
        You will find to your surprise
What is clear and quite transparent
        It just fails to crystallise

Ancient glassmakers discovered
        If a tube were introduced
Air blown in could form a bubble
        Thus glass vessels were produced

Then by adding to the mixture
        Different colours could be made
Using several metal oxides
        Hues of almost any shade

Using light that's streaming inward
        Back from mediaeval times
Stained glass windows in cathedrals
        Glory added to the chimes

Many other types of mixture
        Make the virtues more pronounced
Toughened, laminated, armoured
        Mirrors from which light is bounced

In its cold state, glass is able
  To be cut or ground or polished
But beware the glass at table
  By a singer's voice demolished

Taking sheets of glass together
  With an air-gap in between
Heat and sound are insulated
  But the view can still be seen

Adding boron gives the virtue
  Rapid change of heat to bear
Add some lead for high refraction
  Lenses, glasses, tableware

Glass, like steel, is no invention
  Just a thing for Man to find
Plenty more yet to discover
  If we just apply the Mind

When you next look in a mirror
  Think of glass, reflect awhile
Is that really you you're seeing
  Or a mirage with a smile

Something and Nothing

We may think of something and nothing
    As nothing to bother about
But a certain small something and nothing
    Is what we can't now do without

Now in childhood, as soon as we're ready
    We learn how to count up to ten
Then we learn how to hold that in memory
    And we start off from zero again

Now this is alright to one hundred
    Where the storage itself overflows
And a new layer is desperately needed
    To keep memory itself on its toes

Now this process can go on for ever
    But the memory runs out in most men
So to keep any permanent record
    They have to resort to the pen

With this means of account you're acquainted
    But consider a different mode
Using only the one and the zero
    It is christened the Binary Code

Now instead of each level of storage
    Being ten times the level below
When there's one to add one in a level
    Then to level above both must go

So for two, you've a one and a zero
    And for three, you've a one and a one
So to add any more and to reach up to four
    You've to empty these first and move on

So for four, you've a one and two zeros
    And for five, you have one, zero, one
And with six, one, one, nought, you're beginning to sort
    That your seven's, one, one, one and so on

Now for Goodness Sake, why should this matter?
    You were happy enough up to ten
But the Binary System's essential
    As computers count simpler than men

Now by using electrical charges
    To represent 'ones' in the line
You can store this away at the end of the day
    To await any task you define

You may say, 'What has this got in common
    With my new user-friendly machine?
To talk about somethings and nothings
    Is offensive and rather obscene'

Well, the answer to that is straightforward
            And is truly a matter of fact
That it's only a very few decades
            Since they first learnt to add and subtract

What started with valves and transistors
            And took up the space of a house
Can now be contained on a finger-nail chip
            Which can then be controlled by a 'mouse'

And millions of human brain-hours
            Have been spent to develop the mode
Which takes your instructions in language you know
            And turns them to Binary Code

The size of the 'chip' is important
            To produce the miraculous speed
To search and to process whatever you've asked
            And to answer in what you can read

With a similar series of digits
            You can process both pictures and sound
So just think of your somethings and nothings
            And the wonderful tools that you've found

Greenwich Mean Time

So what can I do with an hour
    An hour elusive but free
For as Autumn is turning to winter
    We're reverting to old GMT

Now, for once, I am properly acquainted
    With this gift in the midst of the night
For to find out too late in the morning
    Can give you a heck of a fright

You may find if you go for your paper
    That the doors of the shop are still shut
Or, if virtue propels you to Matins
    You're left standing there, feeling a mutt

There are those for whom Sunday starts later
    Who prefer to relax in the tub
But their schedule is badly disrupted
    When they can't seem to get in the pub

Now in Springtime an hour goes missing
    And the shock is the same in reverse
If you do not know what you are missing
    The impact of this can be worse

In the Spring, whilst you may lose an hour
    In the evening an hour you gain
And, after the darkness of Winter
    This suddenly softens the pain

You may ask why we change time in summer
    Well, it's mainly the farmers who gain
For it gives them an extra long evening
    The better to gather the grain

There are some who would go Continental
    And have Summertime all of the year
And, in truth, this idea has its merits
    Though its logic's not totally clear

They may argue that accidents happen
    In the dark on the way home from school
But that only shows half the equation
    So who are they trying to fool?

For, if you keep afternoons lighter
    The mornings are darker instead
And a driver still tends to be sleepy
    When he's only just got out of bed

Now, if this arrangement were better
      There are yet no statistics to tell
But if you have been killed in the morning
      You can't be killed later as well

Now, Europe's time also goes summer
      But it changes on different days
So, why be just out by an hour?
      We can also stay right out of phase

There's one thing we're proud of in Greenwich
      And our Meantime we don't mean to lose
For it's here at the point where the East meets the West
      Which the World was persuaded to choose

It was due to our maritime history
      With a little sang-froid, from the French
That a century ago with much glory
      The Primary Meridian did wrench

Now I hope this spare hour was not wasted
      In giving some thought to this rhyme
But it wouldn't hurt some to rise early
      In accordance with Greenwich Mean Time

Food for Thought

When you are sitting at breakfast
        With cornflakes and milk in your bowl
Spare a thought for the children in far distant lands
        Where starvation is taking its toll

They won't be sitting at breakfast
        And probably don't have a bowl
Imagine the pain where their stomachs should be
        And remember each one has a Soul

'So why don't they get off their backsides
        And get some fresh milk from the cow?'
Well, they've never heard about bacon and eggs
        For they haven't got hens or a sow

'Why don't they grow their own cereal?
        It just takes a handful of grain'
Well, they haven't got land that is fertile enough
        And nor do they have enough rain

So what can you do to help children
        Who are living in lands far away?
Well, first you must learn more about them
        So you can assist them, one day

So at school and at home make a study
        Of each country and people and climate
And discover the areas of desert on Earth
        With no hope of sustaining a primate

To see the extent of the problem
Where in Britain there's one mouth to feed
Then in India alone there are twenty or so
And there's thirty or forty Chinese

You may think that you've found a solution
If you say that the deserts must go
But it's sad to relate at this juncture
That these are more likely to grow

We have fiddled enough with our climate
To know what we're doing is wrong
So, one thing we can do to rectify this
Is to voice our concerns loud and strong

You will see as you study each country
That each nation's in some stage of stress
There are some who are tackling the problems
And some in a terrible mess

You may say, ' There are too many children
So stop quite so many being born'
There are parts of the World where this message gets home
And the light is beginning to dawn

But where a man's family is starving
And the prospect next morning is death
Then he'll fight whilst there's strength in his body
Till he finally takes his last breath

So, in places where there are no leaders
And where farmers should rightly be kings
It's for certain they're getting the wrong sort of Aid
For the men with the guns hold the strings

In countries where gun-law is ruling
              The people will flee in the end
For fear of a bullet will drive them away
              Although there are good crops to tend

If nations stop selling them bullets
              And teach about farming instead
Then lands that are bare become fruitful
              And people sleep soundly in bed

If you think, 'Well then, why should I bother
              If everyone knows about this?'
Then you don't know the ways in which governments work
              And your thoughts would be sadly amiss

Now just give a moment to history
              And study the way that folk move
As one place becomes more like Hell upon Earth
              They all seek for room to improve

And Government Aid sometimes broadcast
              Doesn't end in the right hands at all
And what may be given for grain in the Spring
              Swells a Swiss bank account by the Fall

And so, what was rightly intended
              Ends up as a bullet instead
And what was supposed to fill stomachs
              Ends up as a hole in the head

You may have already found sponsors
        To give, if you walk, run or swim
So make sure the money goes where you intend
        In addition to keeping you trim

And when you have built up some knowledge
        You can take a much longer-term view
For, if you don't go out to share what you know
        They'll all come and share it with you

The next need for people is medicine
        Once they have shelter and food
There's room for some more Albert Schweitzers
        If you happen to be in the mood

The next stage is then education
        At first, steps in Do-It-Yourself
But here some big changes are needed
        And not simply West-off-the-shelf

If every developing country
        Follows what we have done in past years
To establish its smoke-stacked industrial base
        We shall realise the worst of our fears

For the Earth is now swamped by pollution
        And there's one simple message to heed
For there's one thing ahead of our water and food
        It's the air that we breathe that we need

If you worry sometimes of the future
      And think, 'What on Earth shall I do?'
You have answered your question in so many words
      If you look, you will see it is true

You've clearly absorbed what is needed
      But maybe you failed to observe
That in air that you breathe and on earth that you stand
      There's a lifetime of work to preserve

If concern about jobs is a problem
      And children fear life on the dole
Then it's time for a spanking-new ball game to start
      Let's move not just the posts, move the goal

It's up to the next generation
      To change economical measures
Reward those who seek to conserve and renew
      Not those who consume the Earth's treasures

The whole World needs modification
      It suffers from greed and from waste
And folk who've forgotten to speak and to smile
      Could achieve far much more with less haste

Do not dwell upon standards of living
      Because money and greed both cause strife
But remember your duty to good Mother Earth
      And that quality matters in life

Hilda Hypochondria

It's Hilda Hypochondria
      Who's riddled with disease
Just back from Alexandria
      With dysentery and fleas

The morning breaks, her stomach aches
      Her guts are filled with grief
Six times as bad as what she had
      When home from Tenerife

Her buttocks bared, no effort spared
      She sits upon the throne
She'll fade away, she'll lose today
      Six pounds or half a stone

The fleas bite here, the fleas bite there
      The fleas play havoc in her hair
But not a flea is ever seen
      Imagine where they must have been!

With any ills, you're not alone
      For Hilda's primed and set to moan
And any ailments you have had
      Then Hilda's had them twice as bad

And every different strain of 'flu
  She's had for weeks and weeks
When you admit you've got it too
  Her's amplifies and peaks

And every common child's disease
  She's had it several times
Plus all the agues that displease
  The rogues in pantomimes

Should you have trouble with your skin
  You thought she couldn't match
No, she's got pimples on her chin
  That blossom to a patch

The meningitis that she had
  When she was only three
Made her, through fever, raging mad
  Bite off her mother's knee

You may recall the time she fell
  To Parkinson's disease
And shakily declared she caught it
  Straight from Sarah Keays

Now gonorrhoea and syphilis
  Burst on her like a chrysalis
But she fought back, and ten feet tall
  She conquered these and warts and all

She's vanquished AIDS three times at least
      And Hepatitis D
And when the next plague is released
      She'll conquer that, you'll see

Each muscle, bone and blood complaint
      So vividly described, you'd faint
Each ear, nose throat and chest infection
      Hilda's had without exception

The only one that she forgot
      Was Alzheimer's disease
That's what she might be suffering
      So don't remind her, please

Now if at last you've had enough
      The wick of life about to snuff
You'll hear St. Peter call your name
      Tranquillity and peace to claim

But thank St. Peter for his offer
      Perhaps some future time to proffer
You'd find on taking this last chance
      That Hilda's got there in advance

The Spirit of Adventure

'The Spirit of Adventure'
   Sounds rather like a ship
Perhaps a modern sound bite
   Perhaps a video clip

Now inbuilt in each one of us
   For better or for worse
The urge is strong to venture forth
   Depending on the purse

For some the urge is satisfied
   Just playing round the block
Some, driven on, are forced upon
   A bigger door to knock

Adventure points down many paths
   Now which one should you take?
This one may lead to Great Success
   That one to Great Mistake

Some record you may wish to break
   Solve problems of the world
Before its time to pop your clogs
   Or find your toes upcurled

The path that looks the straightest course
  May lead across a bog
The one that twists may well avoid
  A minefield or thick fog

This one may lead to Nowhere Fast
  That one a cul-de-sac
This one a lovely leafy lane
  Which circles round and back

But if you ventured out and tried
  Next day to try again
Experience contrives to show
  That all was not in vain

Amongst the paths that you may try
  Are some already trod
To which those with experience
  Will give a wink or nod

Despite advice from those turned back
  Or guide books on the shelf
There'll be some paths that beckon you
  To try them for yourself

There's always someone to suggest
  A shortcut here or there
But shortcuts often have their snags
  So always be beware

From time to time, upon the path
        You'll need to take a rest
Perhaps to ponder what you've seen
        Or guidance to request

And pleasant folks you'll often find
        When you are on your way
Be wary not to stultify
        Or welcome overstay

And here and there, with lures unknown
        You'll tend to lose the urge
But after such indulgences
        You'll find another surge

Sometimes the urge is not so strong
        Why beat a path at all?
When back at home you can relax
        And have a Rave or Ball

The presence of that Urge within
        Is all you need to know
Not how it got there anyway
        Just where it wants to go

The Spirit of Adventure
        Is something that's innate
Like sexual drive, in most of us
        The urge to procreate

For some, the path that's right for them
            May lead to Works-of-Art
For some, to Help-Less-Fortunates
            Or Surgery-of-the-Heart

Philosophers create new worlds
            Their paths to Ultimum
But few can satisfy their urge
            Just sitting on their bum

For persons born with tuneful flair
            A path with music bent
To share their talents on the way
            May be their main intent

Some may dash off, their sole pursuit
            The path to Bars-of-Gold
But come the Satisfaction Day
            A weary tale is told

A few of these, afore they die
            May stop short in their track
And seek some better causes out
            To utilise their stack

For some the choice is obvious
            They head straight for Vocation
For some, alas, it's forced on them
            They slouch to Allocation

Now some appear so lucky
          As they have so many choices
But they freeze, confused and baffled
          By so many beckoning voices

And some fall sick along the path
          Where so far they have striven
If they have faith, then they will find
          A hidden hand is given

At last, the reason's handed out
          On Satisfaction Slope
The view from here is never seen
          By those who chose to mope

You'll only know what drove you on
          When you have reached your goal
It's then at last you can take time
          And tales of yore extol

The reason will be different
          Whichever path you trod
And one or two will have a view
          Whence they believe in God

'And once again the paths will meet
          All lead alike to Thee'

'Till the Earth shall be filled with the Glory of God
          And the Waters cover the Sea'

Odd, No God

I can't believe you can't believe
That you believe in god
I find such avid lack of faith
In one so young, quite odd

Now first there's the story of Jesus
And there's reasonable proof that he lived
But the date that he died leaves us all mystified
For the truth every archive's been sieved

But the question that most vexes doubters
And which led to his death, which was sad
Is the one modern scientists never will prove
And is simply, 'Son, who was your Dad?'

If you've studied some other religions
Then in most a lone prophet appears
Who has cut himself off from the rest of the world
Wrapped in prayer for a number of years

Now look at yourself for a moment
What a wonderful creature you are
The only things missing, the day you were born
Were some sheep, three wise men and a star

Your brain's like a giant computer
Your body's a marvellous machine
But the thing no production line ever could build
Is the little Soul stitched in between

You will know that the print of your finger
            Varies slightly from all of the rest
And the stamp of your own personality too
            Would be different, if put to the test

Now, if God as the father of Jesus
            Is too complex a subject to broach
There's a valuable message that each Christmas brings
            If you take a much simpler approach

For we all celebrate our own birthdays
            But we borrow another with mirth
And we swop all our presents and eat far too much
            When we celebrate Jesus Christ's birth

For at Christmas we all get together
            And forget all our troubles and strife
And we read once again of the babe that was born
            And reflect on the Wonders of Life

If you've read through the teachings of Jesus
            You may find his advice far too meek
For the most certain way to another black eye
            Is to proffer the opposite cheek

If you look past the literal meaning
            There are words to make each of us think
And to live every day in a Christian way
            Is to swim on the tide, not to sink

That Death follows life is a sure thing
　　　　And it's something we all have to face
That our days upon Earth are all numbered
　　　　Till we move on to make some more space

Now Christ died on Friday at Easter
　　　　A date strangely set by the Moon
And the Earth went all dark whilst he hung on the Cross
　　　　As the Moon and the Sun mourned in tune

It's the last little bit of the story
　　　　Which can most leave the mind overstretched
To believe Christ returned to his father in Heaven
　　　　Seems to many a trifle far-fetched

But as childhood's replaced by the future
　　　　And you notice the years rolling by
You'll observe every Soul leaves a memory behind
　　　　What you've done on this Earth e'er you die

Stand back, if you can, for a moment
　　　　And look at the Earth from a star
You will see Man as part of a pattern
　　　　With each person so small from afar

Now assume you are God for a moment
　　　　With each creature and plant to sustain
You've designed a self-balancing system
　　　　But you still need a mega-sized brain

So this minuscule planet in focus
       Which is what its incumbents call Earth
Is a trivial dot near a star called the Sun
       One of billions much greater in girth

If you've now got some sense of perspective
       Put your feet firmly back on the ground
And look out at the Sun and the Moon and the stars
       And think of the space you have found

Then just look at the Nature around you
       At the opposite end of the scale
See the detail that goes into each little flower
       And its scent on the air you inhale

You may think that your lifespan is paltry
       When compared with the history of men
But Man's few thousand years, matched with billions for Earth
       Gives you cause to consider again

Should you think that mankind has control of the Earth
       Then there's one vital point that you've missed
It is Nature providing the life-giving power
       And all Man can do is assist

Now you've thought of the wonders of Nature
       And you've looked at the large and the small
And you've seen how your brief spell on Earth all fits in
       Can't you feel some great power at all?

Ah, I hear all your doubts and excuses
       Why religion can start all these wars?
And why doesn't God help the poor and diseased?
       And why, when you shout, he ignores?

Well, life wasn't meant to be easy
       For some, it may be for a while
But it's often the case that the one who starts last
       Will end at the top of the pile

To survive, Man is destined to struggle
       And this sometimes can lead to a war
But on one side where God is the loser
       On the other, he's just won once more

You may think that God doesn't listen
       But perhaps you misphrased your request
Or perhaps you were deaf to the way he replied
       Through a messenger, at his behest

Now sometimes the greatest of thinkers
       Find some secrets of faith in the end
But you don't need an apple to fall on your head
       To know there's one more round the bend

So you might have reached your conclusions
       But the message from Nature is stark
If you should ignore the sheer power of God
       You're sure to end up in the dark

What stirs within?

I discovered the source of discomfort
        Which was not what I'd come to expect
For a mixture of liverish tinctures
        Was the sensible cause to suspect

It seemed natural that overindulgence
        Was the obvious thing to accuse
In the absence of culinary symptoms
        Then as Grandma would say, 'It's the booze!'

But then after some twenty-four hours
        When even a beer shies away
It is time to call askance of Sherlock
        To bring further deduction in play

It seemed to stem back to a luncheon
        Where a special Hors d'Oeuvre was consumed
And so scrumptious were all its components
        That its innocence had been assumed

The following dinner was gorgeous
        But reluctance to clear up the plate
Should have set off the stomach's alarm bells
        To signal, 'It's something you ate'

A night of acute indigestion
        When now I start blaming the heat
'Shape up to a full English breakfast
        Look sharp, you've a lady to meet'

Ignoring the signs of resumption
        Of ominous rumblings inside
I seek to get on with my programme
        And try my discomfort to hide

I'm striving to hold concentration
        Whilst my bedroom gets hotter again
I await the return of a phonecall
        Whilst trying my cool to maintain

I must try to restore sense of humour
        I wasn't on good form last night
With butterflies plaguing my stomach
        Perhaps an attack of stage fright?

Whilst at first for my meeting I'm early
        It is clear now I'm going to be late
With my head out the window, I'm thinking
        What it's like as a victim of fate

The phone's like a kettle I'm watching
        And my breakfast has just turned to stone
'Go, before those eggs try to rescramble
        Grab your jacket and get yourself gone'

With a superstore fresh out of chocolates
        And to Oundle there's no turning back
So I overshoot straight into Wansford
        And purchase the best-looking pack

On arrival, a drink was most welcome
        An infusion of hair of the dog
But the stomach's instinctive reaction
        Was to treat it much more like a frog

Here I should have reviewed my suspicions
        For it's certainly something to note
If I'm clutching a nice glass of lager
        But I can't get the beer down my throat

I struggle with gurgles till lunchtime
        With fine cheeses, smoked salmon and trout
All my favourite forms of temptation
        But there's something still trying to get out

The stomach remains hyperactive
        And digests what I've downed of the lunch
Like a cauldron the acid is boiling
        And it's surely now time for the crunch

So, by five, I must make my excuses
        It is tactically time to retreat
For it's game, set and match to my stomach
        I must sadly admit my defeat

I return to my hotel in Oundle
      And collapse in a heap on the bed
But I'm soon on my feet in the bathroom
      For relief, shooting tigers instead

I've located the source of discomfort
      To be honest it wasn't a root
Whilst it seeks to defy definition
      I would say it is more like a fruit

Now cucumber's something that I like
      But cucumber doesn't like me
For it started to fight my digestion
      When I turned about twenty and three

Here I gazed at this startling disclosure
      Just a sliver, but half an inch long
There's a man's total future affected
      By something so weak, but so strong

Now as Sherlock came up with the answer
      And traced the offending Hors d'Oeuvre
Was it fate's philosophical finger
      Saying, 'Sorry it's what you deserve'

To this story there must be a moral
      'If e'er with a lady you'd treat
Bother pride, use your specs when you're eating
      And preferably stick to the meat!'

Love is ..... or isn't it?

If money cannot buy you love
       Then why's it so expensive?
And why can marriage end in tears
       With folk in Care Intensive?

Now marriage is a sacred pact
       A bond between two people
Tradition says you celebrate
       With vows beneath a steeple

You take each other, rich or poor
       For better or for worse
Through every problem of your lives
       Until they bring the hearse

So how can marriage end in tears
       With families divided
And children with one parent less
       Their future undecided?

To study this, it's worth the time
       To look into the past
When people stuck together more
       And marriage seemed to last

In day of old, a lucky few
       Reached three score years and ten
As childbirth killed some womenfolk
       And wars killed lots of men

With people dying of disease
          No medicines to cure
Made life a much more precious thing
          Folk loved each other more

Now father's job was to provide
          Enough for all to eat
And mother cooked and kept the home
          All spotless, clean and neat

And children too had tasks to do
          To earn their modest crust
So families managed to survive
          Though many, only just

A minor quarrel that began
          Would finish fairly soon
And if you lost the toothpaste top
          They'd all forgive by noon

A quarrel that was lengthier
          And seemed like it could last
Brought relatives and friends to hand
          To help until it passed

Divorce was most uncommon then
          And usually rejected
And only with good reasons plain
          Was socially accepted

So what has changed? The laws remain
      That make it hard to part
But somehow partners can't maintain
      The vows they made to start

When men worked hard for many hours
      At mostly manual jobs
The women too were raising kids
      And sweating over hobs

But now with kitchens crowded out
      With time-saving machines
You only need to flick a switch
      To wash the family's jeans

And many wives go out to work
      Some household bills to meet
And children come back home from school
      With no-one there to greet

So households that depended once
      Upon each other's help
Each struggles now to help themselves
      Endeavouring not to yelp

The family's panacea
      Is the television set
Which echoes any family stress
      You're struggling to forget

The TV with its visual charms
        Kills conversation dead
And interspersed with soapy feuds
        Puts violence in your head

Now travel is the greatest thing
        For broadening the mind
But restless children fly the nest
        And leave old folks behind

Then growing to maturity
        Themselves a partner seek
They meet a stranger, fall in love
        And all within a week

Where once each partner would have known
        The family of the other
The boy sized up against his Dad
        The girl just like her mother

But now, with families spread apart
        They never really see
How their beloved's folk react
        When taken home for tea

Now some there are who learn to act
        In order to acquire
The things in life they think they want
        Their objects of desire

But such an act will fall apart
        With those who know them well
So watch them with their oldest friends
        It's then that you can tell

So do beware of anyone
        Who won't live with the past
As any future you may see
        Is likely not to last

You may consider this advice
        Is best dismissed as cynical
But when old Cupid's arrow strikes
        It's then you must be clinical

For life is not a discotheque
        One lasting round of fun
You need to check the forward plan
        Whilst basking in the sun

In modern schools, they teach you Sex
        And tell you how to breed
Don't miss the second lesson though
        It's 'How not to succeed'

This knowledge merely serves to put
        The cart before the horse
And marriage hardly features
        Before sexual intercourse

But sex itself has rarely proved
        A crucial stumbling block
It's when one partner ceases
        That the other runs amok

So Sex, explicitly exploited
        Now to money wed
Should put its sorry name away
        And change to Sell instead

In former days the parents matched
        Their offspring to a swain
By linking common interests, thus
        Would loving thoughts attain

This worked more often than you'd think
        The start was pretty grim
But with two families blowing hard
        You'd just the sails to trim

In modern days, the choice is yours
        But should it really be?
Can you expect, with pangs of love
        Objectively to see

Decide upon a likely sage
        Whose judgement you can trust
With humour not yet stultified
        Nor passion turned to dust

Then state your case, your interests shared
   Your interests separate too
Then take your love to be assessed
   By those advising you

For here's the time to take advice
   Not ten years down the road
When lonesome in your misery
   You're ready to explode

You're so besotted by your love
   You vow you'll never part
But take a break, enough to let
   The head rule, not the heart

And if you think your partner's habits
   You can rearrange
The basic personality
   Is something you can't change

And any marriage built for bridging
   Culture, faith or race
Must have an even better start
   If it's to stand the pace

Beware the wiles of commerce
   Drawing you into the net
To wed in haste will leave you
   Plenty more time to regret

Perhaps you've never been in love
   Perhaps you'll never fall
Perhaps you've seen too much distress
   To want to know at all

To choose one word for damage caused
        To personal relations
It may seem strange, but it must be
        The word, 'Communications'

At certain times in history
        Developments are such
That human systems overload
        They can't absorb that much

And now we rush across the World
        By train and car and plane
We've lost the virtue of a home
        Where love and peace remain

We've got a phone, a fax, a screen
        But does that mean as much?
For sure, we're always there in reach
        But still we're out of touch

You may well ask why I should write
        A cautionary tale
When I could, with a lighter heart
        The Joys of Love regale

But home and marriage will resurge
        Men tiring of their toys
Remember that to procreate
        Needs loving girls and boys

Be ready when the flutters start
        'Oh dear, what can the matter be?'
The moment when the sun shines out
        Of his or her anatomy

Genius

You may not be a genius
        But then again you may
For what we term as genius
        Is often hidden away

A genius is not the lad
        With overblown IQ
His early promise heralded
        In Sunday Times review

A genius is never sure
        About the world around
Or if a thought is frivolous
        Or something quite profound

A genius is a person
        Who is rarely understood
As he often thinks in pictures
        And he'd paint them, if he could

The problem to communicate
        When people couldn't care
Might often lead him to the point
        Of absolute despair

A genius is somebody
        Who wishes he were dead
When he can't unscramble everything
        That passes through his head

A genius is lonely
        And forgets his personal needs
But a party to that genius
        Is a simple soul that heeds

Now genius is manifold
        And often something shared
But slicing Shakespeare Bacon-wise
        Would leave him much impaired

So why has genius disappeared
        Or has it just been hidden?
To value something cash can't buy
        In modern terms forbidden?

The rush, the pace, the noise, the smell
        Leaves genius awash
But genius will rise again
        Excessive greed to squash

There's genius within you
        Which needs something to provoke
It may be brief, a touch, a hint
        Or even one small stroke

A genius is only known
        When he's already dead
When other folk take his ideas
        And call them theirs instead

So use the talents that you have
        Exploit them to the best
And, if you were a genius
        They'll tell you when you rest

The Other Open Prison

The subject on which I am rhyming
       Whose full grasp is not yet to hand
Will be known to those who are interned there
       And perhaps by those still on remand

Now prisons are all shapes and sizes
       Kids associate prisons with bars
There are some barless prisons called 'Open'
       Where confinement leaves similar scars

The prisons with bars are for villains
       Who need to be locked in a space
Which prevents further actions of violence
       To members of our human race

The term 'Open Prison' in some cases means
       That although you've committed a crime
You've accepted your sentence and punishment due
       So 'no bars' whilst you're 'serving your time'

There also exists the offender
       Whose screws have in some way been knurled
For his own good as well as for others
       Needs asylum away from the world

Now knurling has different causes
       And we need to explore several scenes
A preponderance to crack under pressure
       Could be traced to hereditary genes

Or damage sustained during childbirth
       May knurl certain parts of the brain
Causing curious unwonted reactions
       Which others may brand as insane

You grow up surrounded by family
In harmony likely as not
But strange things at home which could happen to you
May upset your behaviour a lot

And accidents happen through nobody's fault
Leaving somebody's brainpower off-peak
And sometimes a horrible deed that occurred
Leaves a cerebral hinge far too weak

So legion are factors which might harm the brain
And your mental behaviour impair
Now sometimes these mind-faults are hidden away
But others may cause folk to stare

To venture through life with no damage at all
Is a rarity few folk could claim
For madness and saneness are relative terms
Let's admit we're all mentally lame

With the concept of 'Prison', but 'Open', in mind
Now relate the events I've depicted
And imagine the brain without walls, locks or bars
In a similar fashion restricted

Though damaged for reasons beyond its control
With the faculties it has retained
It can function within its imaginary walls
But, now where it's impaired, it's detained

Now those minds so damaged by permanent cause
Are interned in this prison for life
They are joined on occasion by those on remand
To share in their solitary strife

Society fosters a plethora of brains
       So consider the ends of the scale
The fearless intrepid there up at the front
       The sensitive tithe in the tail

The two ends are joined in a certain respect
       Their urge of adventure is strong
For those at the front in more physical form
       At the rear, in the mind, does belong

Because of their urge to try anything once
       Their casualty rate may be high
And some may be nursed back to health with some help
       Whilst the mortally wounded will die

Now those who fall midway between our extremes
       Whose urges are not quite so strong
They never hit all of these highs and those lows
       Their ambition is more to belong

And there in the middle, just jogging along
       Come Smith, Jones, Mick, Mac and Patel
Patronised in the media for 'following their peers'
       They tend to remain fit and well

Should they stray to the Open Prison at all
       They would surely attend as a group
Then feeling they'd strayed far enough for one day
       They'd return, quite content, from their snoop

Now those at the rear who are wounded in mind
       Open Prison will hold on remand
With help and good fortune they'll not be detained
       Or sentence suspended will land

Now mental experiment takes many forms
        And some more with danger are fraught
Some folk on remand need a temporary break
        Overstretched with the power of thought

A taut bio-chemo-electronic maze
        Quite deliberately misunderstood
The brain won't release what it knows of itself
        If it should and it could, then it would

Frustrated in this most peculiar way
        Their need for asylum to think
To tease an idea from subconscious to words
        Might turn to narcotics or drink

Unable to find the expression they need
        Their torment becomes an affliction
The strength of their input then chases its tail
        And their catalyst turns to addiction

And so to the Open Prison they come
        Sometimes top folk from Science and Art
Where hopefully reaching the wavelengths they need
        Will emerge thence, refreshed, in new heart

Now how does a prison without any bars
        Find inmates to fill it at all?
And how does an inmate who freely walks in
        Start to build an imaginary wall?

The answer to this is a subtle deceit
        Whatever narcotic you use
The chemical substance reacts in the brain
        Be it nicotine, drugs or just booze

Now drugs affect folk in all different ways
A phenomenon funny to watch
Where one man gets drunk on a half pint of beer
The next takes a bottle of Scotch

At first a small measure of substance provides
An uplifting sensation that's nice
But, if such a drug is too potent for you
It can kill you stone dead in a trice

And after the rise, as the feeling subsides
Follows on the regrettable fall
For there, without seeing the face of deceit
You have laid the first brick of the wall

And each time the substance is used from then on
Moderation goes largely unheeded
To reach the same level of 'high' as before
Some more of the substance is needed

And each time the level of substance ascends
Then the wall in your mind rises too
Now look at the mirror and point to yourself
There, the finger says 'It could be you'

At last comes the time when the 'highs' level out
But the lows proceed lower apace
And physical symptoms begin to show up
Whilst to reach enough drugs is a race

As the wall slowly rises, you need to escape
The source of your substance to find
But whilst you are out, you are seeing the world
Through the bars you have built in your mind

You visit old friends, but they put up their guard
        To your problem they have to defer
Now helpless to help you, they have to concede
        And remember you how you once were

They share their reserve with the rest of the world
        Now a place which you seek to avoid
You suspect folk of plotting and slander and such
        These delusions are called 'Paranoid'

As time marches on, you are left in the past
        Surviving one day at a time
With humour declining and mind growing dim
        You may stoop now to lying or crime

With family and friends just a phonecall away
        And with plenty more help on demand
You're only imprisoned by fictitious walls
        It is your choice to stay on remand

So ask any addict who's been there and back
        He's the one who will know far too well
If you just make that call, then the means are all there
        To reclaim you from death and this cell

At length, concentration is harder to hold
        And all your defences are downed
Your feelings are merged into one murky mire
        And in that all your senses are drowned

Addiction has swallowed the whole of your life
        The wall is now too hard to climb
Secure with your substance, you'll leave without pain
        Just put out the lights and call 'Time'

No Epilogue, naturally.

Here is a final poem for the
New Millennium Generation
and my Toast to them,

'Bottoms Up!'

[As I finalise my verses for delivery to the printers, I do so with a heavy heart, for at this early hour of the morning, Diana, Princess of Wales is being prepared for her last journey. May I express here my condolences to her sons, William and Harry. My simple verses are intended to provoke and promote those who are strong in wind and limb and healthy in mind, in order that they may contemplate and pursue similar ideals which this fair lady demonstrated, for people caring for each other and for the future of the World.]

6th September 1997.

Holograms or Holocaust

If sixty thousand holograms

     Were programmed by transputers

They still could fail

     To catch the trail

Of Love, Devotion, Sense-of-Duty

     Gifts of Energy and Beauty

For putting People back in frame

     To feeding Nations, not to maim

We need some Offspring we can Trust

     Before the World turns back to Dust

To stop the trend to Drugs and Drink

     And learn to Contemplate and Think